Prairie Primer

A to Z

by Caroline Stutson

illustrated by Susan Condie Lamb

SCHOLASTIC INC.
New York Toronto London Auckland Sydney
Mexico City New Delhi Hong Kong

ISBN 0-439-25950-9

Text copyright © 1996 by Caroline Stutson.
Illustrations copyright © 1996 by Susan Condie Lamb. All rights reserved.
Published by Scholastic Inc., 555 Broadway, New York, NY 10012, by arrangement with
Puffin Books, a division of Penguin Putnam Inc. SCHOLASTIC and associated logos are
trademarks and/or registered trademarks of Scholastic Inc.

12 11 10 9 8 7 6 5 4 3 2   1 2 3 4 5/0

Printed in the U.S.A.   08

First Scholastic printing, October 2000

To Candace, with love
With special thanks to the Littleton Historical Museum
C.S.

To Chris, Charlie, and Ella—
for believing that painted pies are just as yummy
S.C.L.

A the Alphabet I'll learn

B for Butter in the churn

C so Cozy by the stove

D we're rolling out the Dough

E brown Eggs I mustn't drop

F the Firewood we chop

G for greedy Guinea hens

H the House that calls us in

"Coming! Coming!" we all sing,
on the porch for one last swing.

I two Irons growing hot,
breakfast porridge in the pot

When the bowls are
cleared away...   **J**   a game of Jacks we play.

Long black stockings,
high-top shoes,

K

for Knickers and
Kazoos

L the Lunch pails packed for school

M this trifling, stubborn Mule!

 for one bad Nanny goat,
pulling buttons from my coat

O our Oxen in the pen

P there's Piggy out again!

Sunday morning, dressed for church,
down the road we bump and lurch.

 **Q** for Quiet much too long

R the rafters Ring with song!

Fabric scraps of green and purple, **S** for ladies' Sewing circle

Teetotum spins for fun

U Umbrella shades the sun

Pedals flying, racing speed,

V

a blue Velocipede!

Carved by Papa...
bright and big,

W

new Whirligig

Count the crosses Sister's stitched...
her first sampler made with  X

Y another Year for me
with birthday cake beneath the tree

Z the days Zipped by so fast
but now it's time for bed at last...
now it's time for bed at last.